THIS JOURNAL BELONGS TO

_____

"I'm going to get out of bed" is sometimes the most heroic sentence of the day.

—ELIZABETH GILBERT—

Strength & grace.

Strength & grace.

Strength & grace.

Strength & grace.

Strength & grace.

Strength & grace.

Strength & grace.

Strength & grace.

Strength & grace.

Strength & grace.

Strength & grace.

Strength & grace.

Strength & grace.

Strength & grace.

Strength & grace.

Strength & grace.

Strength & grace.

Strength & grace.

Strength & grace.

Strength & grace.

Strength & grace.

Strength & grace.

Strength & grace.

Strength & grace.

Strength & grace.

Strength & grace.

Strength & grace.

Strength & grace.

Strength & grace.

Strength & grace.

Strength & grace.

Strength & grace.

Strength & grace.

Strength & grace.

Strength & grace.

Strength & grace.

Strength & grace.

Strength & grace.

Strength & grace.

Strength & grace.

Strength & grace.

Strength & grace.

Strength & grace.

Strength & grace.

Strength & grace.

Strength & grace.

Strength & grace.

Strength & grace.

Strength & grace.

Strength & grace.

Strength & grace.

Strength & grace.

Strength & grace.

Strength & grace.

Strength & grace.

Strength & grace.

Strength & grace.

Strength & grace.

Strength & grace.

Strength & grace.

Strength & grace.

Strength & grace.

Strength & grace.

Strength & grace.

Strength & grace.

Strength & grace.

Strength & grace.

Strength & grace.

Strength & grace.

Strength & grace.

Strength & grace.

Strength & grace.

Strength & grace.

Strength & grace.

Strength & grace.

Strength & grace.

Strength & grace.

Strength & grace.

Strength & grace.

Strength & grace.

Strength & grace.

Strength & grace.

Strength & grace.

Strength & grace.

Strength & grace.

Strength & grace.

Strength & grace.

Strength & grace.

Strength & grace.

Strength & grace.

Strength & grace.

Strength & grace.

Strength & grace.

Strength & grace.

Strength & grace.

Strength & grace.

Strength & grace.

Strength & grace.

Strength & grace.

Strength & grace.

Strength & grace.

Strength & grace.

Strength & grace.

Strength & grace.

Strength & grace.

Strength & grace.

Strength & grace.

Strength & grace.

Strength & grace.

Strength & grace.

Strength & grace.

Strength & grace.

Strength & grace.

Strength & grace.

Strength & grace.

Strength & grace.

Strength & grace.

Strength & grace.

Strength & grace.

Strength & grace.

Strength & grace.

Strength & grace.

Strength & grace.

Strength & grace.

Strength & grace.

Strength & grace.

Strength & grace.

Strength & grace.

Strength & grace.

Strength & grace.

Strength & grace.

Strength & grace.

Strength & grace.

Strength & grace.

Strength & grace.

Strength & grace.

Strength & grace.

Strength & grace.

Strength & grace.

Strength & grace.

Strength & grace.

Strength & grace.

Strength & grace.

Strength & grace.

Strength & grace.

Strength & grace.

Strength & grace.

Strength & grace.

Strength & grace.

Strength & grace.

Strength & grace.

Strength & grace.

Strength & grace.

Strength & grace.

Strength & grace.

Strength & grace.

Strength & grace.

Strength & grace.

Strength & grace.